This book is dedicated to the amazing Minnesota Vikings fans who have allowed Viktor to see every corner of this incredible state! SKOL!

thank you to Tyler, Jessie, Caitlin, Demeka, Brandon, Alyssa, Dane, Jackie, Alicia, and Pat, and plenty of others for helping this little dream become a reality!

www.mascotbooks.com

Where's Viktor's Mustache? An A–Z Voyage Through Minnesota

Minnesota Vikings Football, LLC
2600 Vikings Circle
Eagan, Minnesota 55121

CPSIA Code: PRT1119A
ISBN-13: 978-1-64307-139-8

Printed in the United States

Where's Viktor's Mustache?

AN A–Z VOYAGE THROUGH MINNESOTA

A MINNESOTA VIKINGS STORY

by Viktor the Viking

Illustrated by Romney Vasquez

Oh no, Viktor lost his mustache!

Come along with Viktor to search for his mustache.

He needs your help if it's not too much to ask!

A is for Alexandria

Is that Viktor's mustache on the ground,
Below the biggest Viking around?

Big Ole is Viktor's biggest friend.
He measures 25 feet from end to end!

Some say Vikings visited here long ago,
How tall was Ole then? No one knows!

ALEXANDRIA
BIRTHPLACE OF
AMERICA

BEMIDJI

PAUL BUNYAN 1937

B is for Babe and Paul Bunyan

Viktor checked one spot, let's check one more,
Maybe his mustache got lost in folklore!

Have you heard of Paul Bunyan, his trusty ox too?
Paul was giant and Babe was big and blue!

Many tales can be heard about these two,
Is the mustache behind their giant statue?

Up north to Cook County
Viktor heads with a flash.
Is this where he'll find his
beloved mustache?

There's so much to explore
here if you don't mind hiking,
A favorite activity of
Viktor the Viking.

And be sure to stick around
until it's night
To see the sky lit up with the
Northern Lights!

C is for Cook County

D is for Duluth

Near Lake Superior is where
Viktor looks next.
Under the Aerial Bridge is just
one spot he checks.

From the top of Enger Tower,
such a great view,
He sees there's no shortage of
great things to do.

Sailing, skiing, and biking, to
name just a few,
And don't forget hiking, camping,
and running too!

TWIN CITIES ORTHOPEDICS
PERFORMANCE CENTER

E is for Eagan

Is the fate of Viktor's mustache forever sealed?
Or will it turn up at the Vikings' practice field?

This is where the Vikings make their gameplan,
the best place in the world for any Vikings fan.

Nothing but football, as far as the eyes can see,
Viktor thinks to himself, this is the perfect place for me!

F is for Fishing

Viktor is running out of places to look.
Did his mustache end up on a fishing hook?

There are fish in nearly every lake, pond, and stream,
Every avid fisher's dream!

Fishing a lake like Mille Lacs is always nice,
You can even fish when it's covered in ice!

Did Viktor lose his mustache during a game?
Duck, Duck, Gray Duck might be to blame.

Everyone sits in a circle and one friend goes 'round,
Pointing out ducks until the gray one is found.

The game is great, if only everyone knew,
It doesn't get more Minnesotan, you betcha, it's true.

G is for Gray Duck

Viktor's favorite sport is football, but hockey is nice.
Maybe his mustache is trapped in the ice?

In Minnesota, you can play on a pond or a rink.
The game moves so fast, you better not blink!

So tie up your skates, grab two pucks, maybe more,
Pass one to Viktor – he shoots, and he scores!

H is for Hockey

I is for Ice

Will you help find Viktor's mustache, please?
Before it gets cold and things start to freeze!

From castles to icicles, to your nearest lake,
There are many shapes ice can take.

The temperature drops and ice starts to form,
Get your skating in before it gets warm!

J is for Juicy Lucy

Viktor's search for his mustache is tiring; will they ever meet?
Maybe it's time he stopped for something to eat.

Viktor loves Juicy Lucys, with their molten hot cheese,
He may even share his fries, if you say pretty please.

Maybe he's hungry for lefse, maybe hotdish too?
This page is making him hungry, what about you?

K is for Kayaks and Canoes

Is Viktor's mustache in his canoe?
He can't see it anywhere, can you?

Through the Boundary Waters, you can paddle on,
the water is great just past dawn.

Be sure to bring a friend to help you row,
There's no telling where you'll go!

L is for Lighthouse

Viktor's been looking for his
mustache all day,
He should check the buildings that
light up the way!

Lighthouses are important for
every Lake Superior ship,
They shine through the night to
help boats on their trip.

Split Rock Lighthouse is just one
you can find,
Each lighthouse looks a bit
different, they're one of a kind!

MINNESOTA

M is for Mississippi River

To search the Mississippi River, Viktor might need a boat.
If he lost his mustache there, hopefully it can float!

Throughout the state the Mississippi River flows,
through forests, bluffs, and cities, it just goes and goes!

From Bemidji to Winona, through Minneapolis and St. Paul,
It's a great big river, we better search it all!

N is for Nighttime Activities

Viktor spent his whole day searching all over town.
Will he find his mustache when the sun goes down?

Fun in Minnesota doesn't have to end when it gets dark,
that's the perfect time for movies in the park!

Or maybe you prefer concerts instead?
See one at the Bluestem Amphitheater in Moorhead!

O is for Otto the Otter

When will the search for Viktor's mustache end?
Maybe he could ask his giant otter friend?

Otto the Otter found his home in Fergus Falls.
He's 40 feet long and 15 feet tall!

After seeing Otto, take the Otter Tail Scenic Byway,
It's a beautiful place to spend a nice day.

P is for Parks

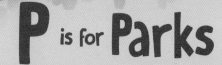

Viktor can't find his mustache anywhere he checks,
Will he have better luck looking in parks next?

The number of Minnesota state parks comes in at 66,
That total gets bigger when you add city and county parks in the mix!

Lake Itasca Park is a beautiful one, of course,
There you can see the Mississippi River's source!

HERE 1475 FT
ABOVE
THE OCEAN
THE MIGHTY
MISSISSIPPI
BEGINS
TO FLOW
ON ITS
WINDING WAY
2552 MILES
TO THE
GULF OF
MEXICO

Q is for Quarries

Will Viktor find his mustache by the end of this story?
It may have been lost when he visited a quarry.

You can visit quarries where they dig 'round the clock,
Some places mine iron and others mine rock.

You can swim and play at Quarry Park in St. Cloud.
At some quarries even scuba diving is allowed!

Viktor's mustache is usually stuck on his face,
Do you think it fell off while watching a race?

There are races of all kinds that Minnesotans do,
Running, biking, boating – some folks race turtles too!

You can cheer and shout at different races all day,
Or drive a racecar yourself at a speedway!

R is for Races

TURTLE RACE

START

Best event of the year? The fair is some people's pick!
Is Viktor's mustache stuck on a stick?

Two million Minnesotans attend the fair each year
to eat cookies, cheese curds, and corn by the ear.

Ride rides 'til you're dizzy or see your favorite band,
Our state fair is the best in the land!

S is for State Fair

CHEESE CURDS

STATE FAIR

TICKETS

FREE
MUSTACHE
GIVE AWAY!

T is for Trails

Viktor's search better not fail,
Maybe his mustache got lost on a trail?

There are trails through cities and trails through parks,
And trails that go past Minnesota landmarks!

Hike, run, or walk, some trails you can skate,
Minnesota has more bike trails than any other state.

U is for U.S. Bank Stadium

Where could Viktor's mustache be?
Did he lose it on gameday? He better go see.

Other teams don't like visiting, the fans get so loud,
Purple shirts, hats, and face paint all over the crowd.

U.S. Bank Stadium is Viktor's favorite place,
Hearing the Skol Chant puts a big smile on his face.

V is for **Voyageurs National Park**

Viktor has no clue where his mustache went,
He thinks it might be lost in his tent.

Voyageurs is the only National Park in our state.
Fishing is popular there, so don't forget bait!

To get to parts of the park you'll need canoes,
But once you get there you'll find amazing views.

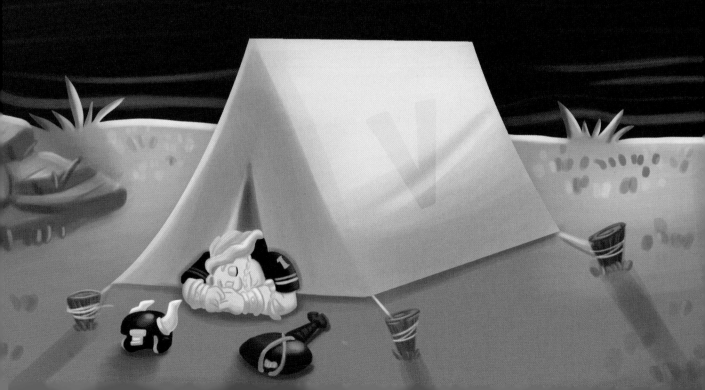

W is for Waterfalls

Viktor hasn't checked any waterfalls yet,
If his mustache is there it'll be soaking wet!

Spring weather means the melting of snow,
that's when rivers really start to flow!

When the river runs out of land, the water drops.
Waterfalls in Minnesota make great road trip stops!

X is for X's and O's

Minnesotans are smart when it comes to their sports,
Did Viktor leave his mustache on a field or a court?

There are so many opportunities to learn,
Different games to play and awards to earn.

Try a new sport, learn with your friends,
With so many choices the fun never ends!

Y is for Yoga

Viktor's stressed out from retracing his tracks,
Maybe his mustache went to a place to relax.

Yoga is the perfect activity to do anywhere you like,
On the rooftops of buildings or after a hike.

At Minnesota Landscape Arboretum you'll see
A yoga class taking place around the trees!

Z is for Zoo

Viktor didn't even know it was something he could lose,
Did his mustache end up at one of the zoos?

Minnesota's zoos take care of animals of all kinds,
From tigers to monkeys, even porcupines!

There's so much to do during a day at the zoo,
To see it all you might need an extra day or two.

Where is the Mustache?

Someone once told Viktor:
"things are always in the last place you look."
Look at that! Viktor's mustache is right here,
On the last page of the book!

Finally, the search for Viktor's mustache is done,
Now it's time for your own fun!
Cut out this mustache and hide it around,
Ask a friend, "Where could it be found?"

Or you can wear it on your face,
When you visit your favorite Minnesotan place!
Send photos to Viktor of your mustache and you,
He would love to learn new things to do!